$100-A-WEEK MOTEL

BY

DAN DENTON

PUNK ★ HOSTAGE ★ PRESS

$100-A-WEEK MOTEL

ISBN 978-1-940213-12-5

Editor
Iris Berry

Foreword
S.A. Griffin

Introduction
Michele McDannold

Cover & Title Page Illustrations
Scott Aicher

Punk Hostage Press
Hollywood, USA
punkhostagepress.com

$100-A-WEEK
MOTEL
BY DAN DENTON
MOTEL
PRINT PRESS
SNACK CAKE
SNACK CAKE
ART BY © AICHER

For Elizabeth

Always & Forever

FOREWORD

Dan Denton's *$100-A-Week Motel* is a hallelujah chorus of proletariat madness, and a fine, sweet madness it is. These stories are a study in wage slave survival behind the gray burlesque of faded curtains pulled tight to hide the unhinged angels of a broken nature. In this modest motel, the circus comes to town, love is possible, sudden heroes wait to punch the time clock and ashtrays overflow with twice smoked twisted butts. As advertised, there is a color television spinning stale reruns casting a flickering light against the remote pornography of the invisible lives that inhabit these rooms. Many of us have been inside these rooms at one time or another. These rooms are where some of us learned to be human, where we learned how to break dance on our last thin dime. Where the broke and broken pray for relief from the shitstorm raging just outside the locked door. That flop where you wake up with the blues for breakfast the morning after you went floating out to sea on a lost weekend that stretched into months. Inside this motel lonely hearts shoot the moon with a pickled magic made of forget me not, and angry young men find themselves in the tender trap of a momentary mercy sealed with a kiss. At this last chance motel, cats live past nine and friendships are born where you can count to ten. There is a cheap bible hiding inside the table at the bedside of every room of this motel that among others, contains the outlaw gospels according to Charles Bukowski, F.A. Nettelbeck and Fred Voss; the poetic catechism of ordinary saints. Skins are shed inside these walls. There is a picture of James Baldwin above the bed in search of self, and no matter how fast or how far a soul might run, heart is where the journey begins and ends, where the home is. And if you press your ear to it, spirituals of the divinely real can be heard inside an earful of peeling paint. Come, let Dan Denton take you to his burning river where you can meet the practitioners of a sincere and wounded faith found only in the lobby of this *$100-A-Week Motel.*

S.A. Griffin
Los Angeles
December 24, 2020

INTRODUCTION

I met Dan Denton for the first time in Toledo at a fundraiser for a mutual friend/mentor, poet Michael Grover. Grover had recently found out he had cancer. Poets and musicians gathered in a place called The Trunk. I begin here because these relationships matter. One thing leads to the next. Grover brings up the poets around him and so I'm in Toledo. Without Toledo, I never would have went to Oakland. Without Oakland, I never would have known Iris Berry, Razor and somehow ended up in the room with Punk Hostage Press. Dan and I keep bumping into one another, there's a chapbook, there's many miles of travels and poems and friends. Then there's a pandemic and there's zoom readings, making connections good for the soul. Well, I'm getting ahead of myself…

It was one of those shindigs, staying alive in the participants minds long after we've all gone home. A big part of that for me was Dan. 1st poem, I'm in. Where did this guy come from?

Turns out, he came from Mattoon, Illinois. A place I'm familiar with, around the way from back home. Cardinal country, just like my neck of the woods. Churches and bars and a highway, just like my neck of the woods. There's something about being a curious person growing up in a place that never changes, people that are scared of change and basically anything or anyone that's different. One of the first poets I got into a regular correspondence with grew up in Mattoon... F.N. Wright. A true outlaw artist and poet if I ever knew one.

I think of Dan and his writing as being an extension of that tradition in the small press. It's the line of the Beats, but dare

I say, more authentic, natural. It's the outlaws running a factory line versus drugs. And like Bukowski, Dan can take you there. Places you wanna be, but maybe not really. People you wanna know because it's so damn interesting, but maybe not the sanest trek. But where Dan steps in and lights a new torch, is, in my opinion, where Buk got it best but only on occasion.

Dan's writing abilities come not only from being a pure, natural talent but for being a goddamned steward of those around him—a man with a generosity of spirit that lights up even the darkest of souls if only for a brief moment. There are people who are made for walking the walk. Dan Denton is one of those people.

As he does for his characters, all find some sort of redemption… in a most sacred way, a way only ink to page can do.

It's true. Dan is a literal union steward. He looks after his brothers on the factory floor as he does his characters, as he does his friends, neighbors and fellow travelers. Meeting them where they're at, in a genuine, honorable fashion. Unafraid to find the beauty and richness of life, wherever it shows up.

To me, this is living poetry in its finest form and brought to a piece of fiction in Dan's own way, fanfuckingtastic! Love in dark places, friends. Problematic saints and saviors. Dan writes in the rhythm of artful, honest compassion; in the tradition of unrelenting, no bullshit this is the real stuff, the honest and true struggle… in every line, loved. It's old school and fresh at the same time. It's Jesus at the *$100-A-Week Motel.*

~Michele McDannold, author of *Stealing the Midnight From a Handful of Days* and *Point of Departure*

It ends well if you don't die.

~ Bob Forrest, Thelonius Monster

1

The tired burgundy door sagged, so that you had to turn your key with one hand and lift up on the knob, loose from being lifted a cunt hair a dozen times a day, and the burgundy paint had long lost the will to live and had given in to the daily thundering pounding of July noon suns.

The air conditioner was the size of a small eco car and grunted and groaned and never quite seemed to hold back summer.

Brown carpet with mysterious stains that told a story of no-fucks-left desperation. Lifeless curtains. Wobbly table. Sagging chair. Queen size bed with mattress ridden hard by boredom and lust. Summer, lightweight, quilt, faded tan with frayed hole near foot of the bed. Mirrors above the bed mounted on the ceiling.

Two drawer dresser. Mini fridge and microwave. Trash can that holds three empty tall boys before slowly vomiting up three day's worth of hopelessness. Sink and mirror. Toilet with jiggly handle. Rust stained shower with dripping shower head. Big boxy tv with free cable and HBO and a two-way switch in the back that clicked the antenna over to a 24-hour adult movie channel.

Jacking off on threadbare bath towels under $6 a bottle champagne splattered mirrors every night at 11pm soaking in the neon glow of hardcore porn and lights out $100-A-Week Motel room has a certain ambiance.

Home is where your heart makes it.

2

Tone and Sheila lived in the room next to mine at the $100-A-Week Motel. Tone sold crack and weed, and maybe a little crank if it was around. Sheila hustled, sometimes cleaned a hotel room for 25 bucks if Moe-the-middle eastern motel owner ever got fed up enough to throw someone out. Sometimes, she'd suck a dick for $40. Or sometimes for $25. I was offered both prices in a hard-up for crack three-day stretch. I declined. Not out of any sense of right or wrong, just because I was cool with Tone and Sheila and I couldn't figure out how that would make anything better. I shared a cheap bottle with them instead. I knew he'd pass a joint next weekend or something. None of us had anything, but we shared what we had when we could. Everyone deserves a chance to be ok for a little bit.

Besides, $100-A-Week motels can be depressing places. Paying your neighbor's wife to suck your dick so she could buy them both crack might have put one of us over the edge eventually. You take those risks with caution. Surviving poverty is a delicate thing to do. It doesn't take an avalanche to bury the poor. Sometimes all it takes is bad luck. Or a pissed off neighbor that knows you have a warrant out for failure to appear in court to answer to two driving on a suspended license tickets.

A week after they moved into the room next door Sheila hung a from-the-everything-is-only-a-dollar-store plastic plaque of Jesus' praying hands on their own tired and sagging motel door. It said, "Bless this home."

I think about that plaque on that door sometimes when I lie awake at night chasing hyper active brain waves down dead-end poetry alleys. Every whore that I have ever known has believed in God.

Home is where your heart lives.

3

I sold things sometimes, too, but I've never developed a head for business. I'd hustle a quarter pound of weed and end up smoking half of it and I'd lose $80 on the whole deal.

I got a job at a printing factory a mile down the road from the $100-A-Week Motel. They printed magazine inserts and Sunday newspaper advertisements. The ones that slip out and fall everywhere and lay in the alley curbs stopping up poor people's storm drains.

I doubt that rich people have stopped up storm drains. But those suburban moms have started hoarding those Sunday advertisements. I suppose if I had a business mind I would know that it's cheaper to buy a dozen bottles of shampoo when they're on sale. Guess all walks of life have their hustles. Some are just more acceptable than others. Some so maddeningly inane that you'll find yourself sticking pins and needles underneath the outermost layer of epidermis on your fingertips, just to see if you feel something.

My first day at the printing factory was eight hours of orientation. Eleven men and one tough woman sitting at tables watching old VHS tapes about how to not walk in front of fork lifts and how sexual harassment is bad. We filled out 23 forms so the government could satisfactorily and without any bumps or hurdles, take a third of our money.

The pay was $8 an hour, almost $3 an hour more than the minimum wage, so a good job. Halfway through a day of staying awake, enduring levels of boredom that rival a sugared up kid living in a trailer with no working TV, when a big redneck fella that had already told everyone he was from Oklahoma asked "What's the policy on if we get caught fighting?" and the tired 53 year old Human Resources training lady said, "Huh?" and the big redneck from Oklahoma went on to say, “I got backed in a corner once by three guys on an oil well in Oklahoma and I had to fight my way out, but I ain’t trying to get in no trouble here.”

We went to lunch after that but lunch wasn’t provided, only a 30-minute period of time that was unpaid. I drank a Mountain Dew and chain-smoked five cigarettes standing just outside the factory on cracked and oil stained asphalt. Nicotine and caffeine are staples of most every factory lunch. They keep you mournfully alive while dead skeletons work all around you.

4

There is a constant stream of new neighbors when you live in a $100-A-Week motel. You don't need an ID to check in, or even a real government name. Just a $100.

First time I walked into the little office to see about getting a room, I noticed the rules listed on a large piece of poster board written in sharpie. The poster board was white at some point in its life. It was yellow then, with curling corners burgeoning against pieces of tape so old that they'd lost their adhesiveness twice in the last decade. Years of tobacco smoke and burnt curry had not been kind to the sign.

Rules written in poor penmanship and poor sentence structures by American junior high school standards. The ones that teach you the 1, 2-3, 2-3, 2-3, 4 power paragraph. Those classes never teach kids that power paragraphs rarely contain any semblance of structure. These sentences had no power either.

"NO ALLOW DIVING AT POOL" one rule said, but the pool served only as a puddle catcher and garbage collector for many years before my tenancy. How can that rule have any power when even the almost criminally insane that frequented the premises would never consider diving into a pool so bereft of anything considered fun and relaxation that it had long ago become embarrassed about being called a pool?

Any of the other rules that might still apply to living in Moe's $100-A-Week Motel were so powerless that everyone openly ignored them. If rules were made to be broken then these rules were the best rules ever made. They were broken, ignored and spat at daily.

"NO VISITOR ALL NIGHT" was my favorite one. I could never figure if the original author intended no visitors at night, or no visitors staying the whole night. Didn't matter anyway. Half the people that slept in rooms there had never stepped inside the office, and nearly everyone that lived there was so broken and incomplete that they needed rather than wanted a warm body next to them while they attempted to navigate nightmares so horrendous that Freddy Krueger, the scariest man that ever lived in Hollywood, only visited during daylight hours.

Home is where comfort is, even if that comfort is toxic.

5

I got put on second shift at the printing factory. 3pm to 11pm, six evenings a week.

As a new guy I got the entry level job. I had to keep an eye on four printing presses. Each press had two guys on the end that watched mountains of shiny paper pile up on their pallets, and when those pallets got full I was supposed to be ready with a pallet jack to move the pallet over to the label station where I would wrap the pallet up in plastic wrap, slap two labels on them, then pallet jack them over by the shipping dock so the fork lift could load them in trucks.

That's easier than it sounds. A mountain of a million shiny papers weighs about 350 pounds. The presses filled a pallet up in five minutes, and with four presses running you were always one or two pallets behind. It was always hot because it was July in the Midwest and everyone knows it gets hotter than Satan's ball sack in July in the Midwest. So you'd be pulling these heavy-ass pallets around all night, sweating your dick off and swearing to the patron saint of rundown factory workers.

You learn real quick to make sure the plastic wrap goes around the bottom of the pallet, too. If you don't make sure, the fork lift driver will jostle it around and a mountain of paper will slide off the pallet and you'll have a snowstorm blizzard of next Sunday's ads knee deep for days. Cleaning up a spilled pallet will ruin your whole fucking night, but it makes everyone else's better. The press operators and loaders would stand there laughing while the Napoleonesque floor boss would stand there red faced and screaming, sweat and spit flying around the humiliated shipper. I only spilled one pallet. It happened on my first day. I waited til the boss quit yelling and left and I got a big snow shovel we used as a dust pan and I shoveled up all the papers into a dumpster except some press operator snitched on me and the floor boss came back pissed and wrote me up for scrap losses of $240. I got wrote up on my first day in the factory.

Weeks later I got drunk at the bar we went to on Friday nights after work and the snitch operator was there and I had about a dozen shots of warm no-name whiskey when I'd finally had enough. You can only share the same oxygen with a spineless coward for so long before feeling the urge to insult his mother, so I did. And he pussied out and looked the other way so that I could see his ear, and half of one eye and just the corner of his stoic lips twitching in perfect rhythm with time and space but just perceptively if one knew the rhythm to look for.

I laughed and went outside and threw a brick through his truck's windshield. Walked home, a mile and a half, drunk and full of myself at 1:30 in the morning.

There are a lot of burned out humans with shorted out wiring always circling the $100-A-Week Motel. My favorite was Rudy. Rudy was 45 but looked 60 and was the most dedicated crackhead I ever met, 'cept Rudy was alright and wouldn't steal nothing from nobody real, 'cept maybe a little something from the corner gas station when he got hungry or a pint bottle of turpentine laced wine when he ran out of money on the fifth of every month after an epic five day crack binge.

Rudy got ran over by a car and dragged for half a city block by a drunk driver. He was panhandling on a busy corner at two in the afternoon when a drunk dude with insurance and nothing much else to live for smoked him and fucked over his whole existence.

A couple people that had been around here a while said Rudy was special before the drunk driver tried to smear him like a bug. I don't know how he was before all that, but he walked with a limp cuz they had "to put my hips back together with wire" and "I got a metal plate right here in my fo' head but you can't cook no dinner onnit," as Rudy said.

Rudy did the same fucking thing every fucking month. He got a disability check for $800 on the first. He paid Moe a month's rent and spent everything else on crack until the money was gone on the fifth. You wouldn't see him much for five days. He didn't sleep. He didn't eat. He smoked crack like a disabled rockstar until every fucking penny was gone and he'd come limping back to the $100-A-Week Motel, looking for a shower, a beer, a meal. Anything to remind him that he was still a value to humanity.

Everyone tried to get Rudy to change, 'cept me. Even Tone next door quit selling him crack. Told him to save his money and only buy a little each day and make his money last all month.

I never bothered. I knew that some humans are like the ocean: there are powerful magnetic forces out there that dictates their behavior. An ocean can no easier stop her high tide than Rudy could stop smoking until he was broke.

After those five days though, Rudy was always around. He did stuff for people for money. It was the only way he survived from the fifth to the end of the month. You could give him $5 and he'd run to the gas station for three loosies and a bottle. Give him a dollar when he gets back and share the bottle a little and he'd run off to find a way to get another buck and by the end of the day he'd eaten a little, gotten a little drunk and he'd have enough for a dime or two for his pipe in the evening and I ain't gonna lie, Rudy was the happiest human I ever met and I was jealous.

Home is where the heart is supposed to be happy, but nobody thinks about being happy when they're spending 100% of their energy trying to survive.

7

The printing factory was a motherfucker. 3pm - 11pm, six fucking nights every fucking week and it ain't like you're hanging out with the cream of the crop of humanity when you're sweating your dick off in a shit-hole, don't-give-a-fuck-about-no-one-but-making-them-presses-run-motherfucking-factory.

I walked a mile to work and back every day for two weeks before them crazy fucking HR people hired Eugene. Eugene was a few years older than me, a white boy, too. Tall and skinny and probably autistic but we didn't know fuck-shit about autism yet back then, so they hired him in at the printing factory and they stuck him on the four presses next to mine. There were 16 presses and four shippers and of all places I got stuck next to Eugene which wound up being ok, for a while.

Eugene lived with his momma still, and he had a little two-door rusty Chevette that back fired every three fucking blocks, but he started giving me a ride to work and back every day for $10 a week, and just because I wasn't a complete dick to him all the time.

Everyone else in the printing factory was, though. A dick to him. They made fun of him, picked on him, laughed at him, played tricks on him and made his life hell. Shit-hole factories are some of the most unfeeling, numb and heartless places in the world. A bunch of roughneck men and even tougher women, none of 'em finished much high school, and none of 'em dreamed of going to college. So you wind up with a bunch of tough stupid people just standing around waiting for something, anything different to happen. Then comes Eugene.

That stupid fucker would never stand up for himself and that used to piss me off almost as much as the full-grown adult bullies did. I fucking hate bullies because I was a weird kid in the projects and everyone tried to whip my ass when I was little and then I'd come home all beat and bloody and my old man would whip me again for being a pussy. He whipped me all the fucking time, but always more if he thought I was being a fag or a pussy. Eventually you learn ain't no one going to stop everyone in the world from whooping your ass if you don't stand up for yourself. So one day after school I fucking snapped.

There were two kids in fourth grade that lived in my projects when I was in third grade. Trent and LaVar. They were both held back so they were big fourth graders and every day after school they would chase me home and beat the shit out of me. I tried running but then my Dad beat the shit out of me for being a pussy, so I just started trying to fight back but fighting two kids bigger and two years older wasn't fair and I got stuck in a cycle of getting stomped then sneaking home and hoping the old man would be too drunk to see I got beat up, again, so he wouldn't beat the shit out of me, too.

Until one day when I snapped and I picked up a fucking brick and held it next to my leg kinda hiding it until Trent and LaVar walked up and those stupid fuckers were smiling cuz they were too fucking dumb to wonder why I wasn't running and I cracked Trent in the fucking head with the brick and he just stopped and pitched forward face first and didn't move with blood spilling in a puddle off the sidewalk into the street and I took off running but someone saw it happen and called the cops so I got arrested when I was seven.

Trent didn't die, but he did stop fucking with me and so did a lot of other people and I learned something about survival: no one fucks with you if you're crazy.

Also, my old man had to get the neighbor lady to drive

him to the police station to get me cuz we didn't have a car. He apologized to the cops and never was more polite than right then in the police station. He took me home and beat the shit out of me for ruining his evening like he couldn't reschedule his drink until you pass out in the fucking recliner for one night.

But it didn't matter because I'd lost all respect for my Old Man. He was scared of cops and I saw him kissing their ass and I hated him for being a pussy. Get a brick, motherfucker.

So the only thing I learned to hate more than a bully was someone that was too chicken to stand up for themselves.

And then there's fucking Eugene trying to work in a printing factory. I'd yell at him once a week on our way home, even though yelling at him made me feel guilty. I was stuck. Always telling the operators and loaders and fork lift drivers to fuck off and leave Eugene alone, and constantly being pissed at Eugene for just taking their shit.

Life is always just like that. For 42 years now, always just like that. Always fighting everyone and being pissed at the ones you're fighting for/with. They won't teach you that in junior high.

8

I was hanging out with this Puerto Rican chick named Juanita for a minute. Nita was about 19 then, around five foot tall 100 pounds, meaner than a one-eyed cat and gorgeous as fuck. Me and her cousin Reno delivered furniture together til I lost my license for driving drunk. Moving company fired me, and Reno cuz he couldn't drive either.

Nita brought me a plate of beans and rice and tacos her mama made, before work one Friday. I'd gotten up early and rode down to the printing factory with Eugene to get our paychecks. I brought home $298, $293 after cashing it at the corner store about $260 after a carton of smokes and a 12-pack of Natty Light. $160 after paying rent and $140 after an eighth of weed from K-rock in room 18.

And now about two hours before work me and Nita were sitting at the rickety table with the curtains open. I was in my boxers eating and reading a paperback copy of some Camus. Nita was watching tv and smoking a square when I saw an old, short school bus drive in the Motel parking lot. I stopped reading and watched 'em drive past the window, and Nita sensing I'd stopped reading a second and said, "You ain't wanta talk today? Or you gonna read til you go to work?"

"Fuck you care?" I asked.

Her head flinched.

"I was gonna suck yo dick," she said.

"Still are," I said, "get me a beer."

And I got up and went to the door and stood and looked down the way at the bus parked by the office. I lit a Marlboro, or a 'cowboy killer' as Tone called 'em. A tall, skinny, wild-looking dude got out the bus and went in the office. Dude looked like he was a European hippie or something.

"Get your own beer," Nita pouted.

I turned and looked at her and she got up and got a Natty, opened it and brought it over.

I drank a third, hit the Marlboro and went back in and laid down.

"C'mere you baby bitch," I said and she did.

Home is where you eat and fuck.

9

There is a universal sadness in every factory I've ever worked in, no matter the position on the Fortune 500, or lack thereof. I've worked in bright, clean, full-of-bullshit faux cheer factories and I've worked in shit hole, rat sewers that were so disgusting we'd walk down to the corner gas station on break so we could shit. Think about that. We willingly sought a gas station bathroom in the projects over a workplace shitter. Dude owned the gas station loved it. Kept it half clean and sold us beer and smokes and lottery tickets and crack pipes, and two day old soggy pre-made sandwiches.

Universal sadness and a certain kind of sick fucking poetry. Machines marching a grinding cadence. Machines growling at half alive men, half dead men. Machines hypnotizing American workers into thinking that hard labor will someday pay off and if they just save their pennies in their 401k, they can retire comfortably.

Universal sadness. Men torn from broken beds with empty lovers. Men leaving corrugated cardboard apartments and houses, driving banged up rusted up sheet metal trucks, living corrugated, cardboard lives.

But I'll be motherfucked if there ain't a certain Zen to the madness. A certain rhythm that gets under your skin and spills into your bloodstream and the hum of the factory becomes a mantra that oms its way through stale August evenings.

There's a certain satisfaction, a certain pride that comes from a back sore from work. From tired feet and heavy shoulders, aging hearts, and flecks of paper dust settling in your hair. A certain chip-on-your-shoulder feeling walking out of a factory at 11pm, tired and sweaty, your work boots 3 ounces lighter from just being off the clock. A certain happy feeling walking away with the chatter of capitalism fading and smiling visions of ice-cold beers lifted by work hardened muscles and tired hands, rough from a thousand times pulling a pallet jack around a factory floor.

Yeah man, there's poetry in the factory. But ain't nobody at the printing factory understand that.

They will always look at you funny in a factory if you carry a paperback book in the back pocket of your jeans.

10

Six people moved into the two empty rooms at the end of my side of the Motel. I was fifth from the end, so they were two rooms down. Two men and four women. Troubadours. Jugglers. Seers. Jewelry makers. A sword swallower.

At one point in American pop culture, they would have been called Gypsies, but the ethnic Gypsies have reclaimed their heritage. At another point in pop culture, they would have been called freaks, but America has grown a little sensitive to name calling. I tell you these things without judgment. We called them by both names when they were my neighbors in the $100-A-Week Motel, and whether right or wrong, they owned both monikers, and then some.

Looking back these two decades later, I'd call them free-spirits. Then again, sometimes I remember the things I knew of them, and I wonder if there is such a thing as a person being truly free. If the free-spirits that roam the land like driftwood, like tumbleweed, like freight cars wandering lost across midwestern farmlands, if those people still struggle with inner-self prisons of self-doubt, insecurity, body-dysphoria, bipolar disorder, borderline personality disorder, bulimia, PTSD, ADHD, dandruff and dry scalp, eczema, gonorrhea, crabs, pneumonia, and poverty, then what hope is there for true personal freedom?

Home is where you think about things.

11

We went on like that, Eugene picking me up from the Motel every day at 2:30, riding to work, sloughing through eight hours of tedious, monotonous madness, then Eugene taking me home to the Motel at about 11:30 every evening, except on Fridays when I went to the bar after work and tried to hitch a ride home from there with someone else.

After a month, I got a quarter an hour raise, which after 48 hours worked every week, came out to an extra $13 a week. I was eligible to buy into the company healthcare then, too, but when you're bringing home $300 a week working full-time, paying $75 a week for health insurance isn't really an option.

Eugene kept getting picked on, and I kept sticking up for him if it got too bad, and I kept getting pissed at him for being a pussy, and the whole thing was just one energized chaotic cycle that I couldn't get the fuck out of and mostly just made me despise everyone all the time, which wasn't a whole lot different than all the other times in my life.

Then one day Eugene asked if I wanted to come to his Mom's house one Sunday afternoon for his birthday. I remember it was a month or more before my mid-September birthday, so it had to be in August, and I really the fuck did not want to go to Eugene's Mom's house on the afternoon of my only fucking day off, but he had already told me he didn't invite anyone else because he didn't know anyone else that might like to come. He was turning 25. So I told him me and Nita would come and I thought he was going to cry when I told him yes which made me feel a little shitty for not wanting to go.

Nita didn't want to go more than I didn't want to go. "Why I gotta go to the retard's birthday?" she kept asking, and it kept pissing me off, and I kept telling her not to call him that, and she kept being pissed until I told her to either go with me, or fuck off, because I did not have the energy or desire to argue about going to a birthday party that I didn't want to fucking go to either, but couldn't see any way of not going. Also, there wasn't yet a public proclamation that we couldn't say the "R" word, and I tell you that without judgement. I'm not saying I didn't ever say it, but I knew it was wrong to call people it. Nita went with me to the party.

We walked the three blocks down to Eugene's Mom's house. I'd bought him two packs of smokes, two Mountain Dews, a couple of scratch off tickets and a Chicago Bulls hat, all from the corner store, and carried it to the party in a shiny red bag that cost $1 at the everything's-a-buck store. We got there and his Mom was there with her Mom and Dad, his grandparents as that's all the family he had, which is a hell of a lot more family than most of us at the $100-A-Week Motel had.

There was fried chicken from the local grocery, and potato salad, and cake and ice cream. Eugene's Mom had two poodles, and they were always yapping around and giving me a headache, but Nita loved them and kept holding them in her lap, and letting them lick her face and trying to get me to say how cute they were. I wasn't sure if she was trying to piss me off on purpose or not. Eugene's grandpa was a deacon at some local non-denominational church, and he kept telling me how I really should come by one Sunday morning if I was looking for a church home. I was trying to be polite, and I was trying to find a way to get the fuck outta there, when Eugene's Mom told him to take the poodles out for their "potty break."

Soon as he was out front with the two mop-head looking yappers running around on leashes tripping him up every third step, we sat watching when his Momma said, "You know he still wets the bed every night, which is just as well. Won't find no wife like that, and guess I'll never have to worry about an empty nest." And his grandpa pitched in some opinions about his bed-wetting and how maybe he was being coddled too much, and Eugene's Momma got mad and started crying and yelling about how Eugene's Grandpa would never understand what it was like raising a man on her own since Eugene's Daddy had run off with some whore and Eugene walked back in with the dust mop yappers and unsnapped their leashes as we all froze there, Eugene's Momma sobbing with snot bubbles falling on her fat titties and Eugene's Grandpa sitting there with his arms crossed and Eugene acting like nothing was the matter helping himself to a second helping of cake, and looking over his sobbing Momma asked me, "Yo, want more cake?" And I saw my exit, "No thanks Eugene. We gotta go."

And we did. Walked back the three blocks, then one more to the corner store where I bought a case of Natty and a bag of pizza rolls and we both went to the Motel without saying a single word to each other the whole time, saddened into a state of despair.

Guess it's better sometimes if you get to pick your own family.

12

One of the women from the traveling troupe of wandering entertainers was a lady named Raven. Raven would come over sometimes if I was sitting outside and bum a smoke from me and ask me about the book I was reading. Raven liked to read, and I was pretty much the only human in the $100-A-Week Motel that owned more than two books, not counting the Gideon Bible, standard in every motel in America. If Bibles were food, the Gideon's would feed us all.

Raven started coming down and talking with me and shit, and Nita didn't like it and we got into a big fight and I told her to fuck off one too many times, and she did, and she was gone and never came back.

Raven was a life advisor. She read palms, read tarot cards, believed in horoscopes, played guitar and didn't shave her pussy. I found out about that last part a few days after Nita split. 72 hours of ignored phone messages and I figured I was fucking free enough.

Raven read my tarot cards. The death card never showed up. Told her it figures. I'd been playing craps a die short my whole life.

Home is where the odds are supposed to be in your fucking favor.

13

I got wrote up again about a week before my birthday. I got into it with one of the loaders that was fucking with Eugene one day. He was this little asshole prick of a guy, going bald with a ponytail still, about two inches taller than the minimum to ride the scariest ride at the county fair, and a city block full of attitude to make up for it. That kind of fella. He was a volunteer firefighter in this little village outside town, and he walked around telling stories about drinking beer with the other volunteer firemen and fighting fires and saving babies and shit. I was pretty certain I'd been involved in more structure fires than he'd ever seen in his life, and most of 'em I didn't even start.

One day he must have been bored, and emboldened with the group mentality of two other monosyllabic, tobacco chewing idiot loaders, who were double dog daring him to ever heightened lengths of cruelty, and just about the time the diminutive macho man got around to asking Eugene how his momma's pussy tasted to the hysterical delight of his fan club, and I snapped and picked up a six foot industrial floor fan and flung it at them. The fan flew all of 11 feet and skidded at them just enough so they all had to dive out of the way as the fan smacked into the press behind the idiots 'R' us weekly meeting, tearing the web of paper out and causing 37 minutes of production downtime and the loss of one floor fan. The short, potbellied floor boss got pissed about it and gave me a fucking lecture about how I didn't appreciate the chance I had here. After 20 years he was making $65k a year and putting a kid through college, and if I just gave a fuck and showed up and did my job I could get my balls snipped and say "yes sir" all the time when some middle manager boss couldn't get laid three days in a row, and decided to tell me how shitty I was at my job.

"Yeah, man," I said, adjusting my ass on the plastic chair in his little fucking glass cube in the middle of the fucking noisy ass factory floor. It's uncomfortable sitting with a paperback copy of a James Baldwin novel in the back pocket of your Dickie's work jeans.

The boss sat there sweating and talking and I was smiling the whole time wondering what he would say if he knew I was thinking about a book in my back pocket written by a gay black man while he was living in France? France seemed like a million miles away. I bet the fucking floor boss doesn't even know where it is on a map.

14

Tone and Sheila got in a bad fight one night when I was at work and Eugene had to drop me off on the street in front of the $100-A-Week Motel because the parking lot had about a dozen cop cars.

The details were always a little fuzzy and involved Tone shooting two bullets through his ceiling and scaring the fuck out of ole crackhead Rudy who was drinking a tall boy, laying in bed in his boxers watching the 10 o'clock news, when bullets ripped through his mattress less than a foot away from his right foot before finally lodging in his ceiling.

Tone was a felon. He wasn't supposed to own a gun. And they found drugs. And another gun and Tone was gone, heading the wrong way up a real shitty creek.

Sheila was busted up a little and crying about Tone being arrested. Even dysfunctional love is love.

She made it just a few more days, moping around bitching about how Tone was gonna be so pissed at her and how she couldn't even suck dicks cuz her mouth had six fucking stitches in it.

Moe evicted her the day after she missed her first week's rent, and got pissy with me when I told him he was a dick for that, but he coulda gave her a day or two, heartless prick.

Sheila moved on with another low-level street hustler that had a trailer in SunRay Village Mobile Home Community about a mile up the road from the Motel. She left her "Bless this home" sign on the door and some chick from down the other side of the Motel took it and put it up on her door. Hope it worked better for her than it had for Sheila.

Home is where love bruises, and heals.

15

Eugene didn't show up one day and his mom answered the phone when I called him and told me he was sick and had a fever and wasn't going to work. I said fuck it and called off and got fucked up with Raven, staying up til seven in the morning, yelling poetry at the cracks in the corners of the hotel room and Raven sat naked in the middle of the bed, playing her guitar and singing Janis Joplin songs.

I took the bus to work the next day, hungover and hurting. The short fat boss wrote me up for my attendance occurrence and tried to lecture me again about the great job opportunity I had, but I cut him off short. My head hurt too much to concentrate anyway.

At lunch, I walked down to the corner gas station and bought a pint of wine and drank about half of it before I got back to work, and I felt loose. Felt better.

I sipped the rest over the last few hours of my shift, and wondered why I didn't drink a little at work more often.

16

A young white trash couple moved into the room that used to be Tone and Sheila's. They were junkies, and were always trying to bum smokes off me and shit. Once, the dude, I think his name was Chris, asked to bum a pack of smokes.

"A whole pack?" I asked.

"Figured it'd save on asking you for another square tomorrow," he said.

I gave him a smoke and told him to get fucked. He shrugged and bummed a light.

I hung out with Raven and her traveling troupe of misfits. They were jugglers, sword swallowers, pickers and singers, acrobats, magicians, witches and wizards. They lived on the rebuilt short school bus and travelled around together going from town to town and festival to festival, trying to earn a buck.

We'd hang out and trade stories, smoking and drinking tall boys and pint bottles of wine. It was a way to pass the time without having to let parts of your brain get melted by day time game shows.

Raven went away one weekend on the school bus of intergalactic prophets and I was bored as fuck, and cagey. I'd just finished a Robbins novel, and hadn't started a new book yet, and being in between books under a full moon ain't no place for a lonely man to be.

I knew everything about psychiatry, because my Mom got me scholarships to maximum security state hospitals by attempting to commit suicide no less than three times per year until I was 11.

But I didn't yet know fuck shit about being bipolar. It's hard to figure it out through despair and crack smoke. I didn't know that full moons would raise high tides in my dopamine levels, and I'd go manic, dancing with darkness and chasing higher highs.

It was Sunday. Raven was in Ann Arbor bewitching sorority sisters with her divinity, and it was fall, gray and raining so fine and steady, like the man's boot on a poor man's throat, ever weighing heavier minute by goddamn minute, until the hours grind away at your voice box and you choke on dust, dying at 68 of lung cancer in a pink tin can trailer in Orlando, two fading plastic pink flamingos dying in a two swipes of a plug-in lawnmower front yard.

I wasn't going out like that. Not when the moon was so full that you could see it fighting back behind the rain clouds, and bursting through just enough to give off a weird green night sky, heavy with rain and frustration.

I walked down to the corner store in an Ohio State hoodie, hood up against the boot of the man falling from the heavens.

I saw Nita there with some fat fuck nobody punk. I bought a bottle while Nita stood smirking in front of me in line dry humping the fool. I laughed and shouldered him a little as he passed and he turned and made tough noises at my back. Nita pushed him away. I said "That's right. You're both bitches," and laughed in the rain back home.

I drank the bottle watching Sunday night football through a shimmer of nervous energy and fueled by a river of rage flooded by a lifetime of unfair treatment by Jesus' government of holy kid fuckers. I walked over to the dive bar across from the $100-A-Week Motel and I spent two days' pay on real liquor and stumbled home with a white girl in a jean jacket, pancake makeup and cowboy boots. We got high and listened to the rock station on the radio and we started fucking, but I was drunk and angry and bored.

She got on top and started calling me Daddy but she was 40 and I was 20nothing and the whole thing was so ridiculous I pushed her off and got up to smoke. She sucked my dick while I smoked, and fell asleep just after I finished, her breath warm on my crotch, and I stared at the dying wall of a don't know if I'll ever make it out of here alive sadness that seeps under the door of an off-kilter $100-A-Week Motel.

Home ain't home if you ain't even there.

17

The factory was dead on Monday. I was, too.

That's the thing about a factory, they're living organisms. Unfeeling, but living, and they have moods. Energy. You can feel it in the air all around you. Might be something about the vibrations in a machine working themselves into a man's DNA to where the factory and the man are connected involuntarily.

There are blue energies, when busted radios with duct taped coat hanger antennas play local rock channels, used car commercials competing under the hum of the machines while black afternoon rains pound shipping dock concrete. Blue days, where no one talks, they just endure.

There are plain days, when the machines run themselves and factory men and women leave their brains at home to dwell upon desperate family situations. Days so forgettable that no one is sure they happened, except there's a days pay for it on your check and the company stock sure as shit went up 2%.

Payday Friday's are the best days in the factory. Everyone orders lunch delivered, and hidden flasks appear. Lottery ticket daydreams are laughed about and elevated with heavy pocket camaraderie. The tavern down the road beacons like a homing device for hope-thirsty laborers.

Dead Monday's are tough energies to survive. The machines hum their efficient mantras, as the acceptance of our universal role of stoop backed boot wearing tax ID numbers is forced upon us, and in us, until we drown in the realization that we will never rise above this level of working-class enlightenment. No one wins the lottery. No one ever wins the new car given away at the pink slime fast food chain grand opening. No one ever guesses the correct number of jelly beans to win a $100 toy store shopping spree. No one wins in the factory.

You'll show up every day, week after week, and the hot dog at the annual family day picnic is still just a hot dog and your 401k will limp along on life support. A dinghy in the ocean of Wall Street sharks and cancer scare stingrays.

You'll watch a time lapse of wrinkles appear on foreheads and gray hairs at temples and bellies above belt buckles and limping trick knees stumble away into forgotten afterlifes of boxcar humans waiting alone with TV dinners and paperback books hoping you have enough cheap packs of cigarettes left to make it til first of the month when social security checks bleed through rusty Florida mailboxes.

Dead Mondays are hard to survive, but if you do, Tuesday will come knocking and you'll be in the middle of next month again, numb to the machine vibrations that rock you to sleep in the creaking queen-sized bed of a $100-A-Week Motel.

18

Raven was back and bitchy because she found out about the 40-year old Sunday night visitor. We didn't argue about it or nothing, she just seemed distant and my head was still struggling to contain the burgeoning dopamine levels that manic episodes bring. I paced and didn't sleep and fucked around with Raven but neither of us talked much and everything just seemed a little uneasy.

The white trash couple fought every day and fall snuck in with the realization that summer was gone and so too, were the hopes of saving enough money to buy a one-way train ticket to Florida before winter roared across the Midwest.

Raven finally came back around and the edginess of chaos wore down some and she started staying every night in my room and we were hardly ever alone except when I went to work. The traveling tour of scrape up a buck by any trick was floundering and the troupe was bickering and arguing about whether to take off and chase greener festivals or to bunker down for the winter in the $100-A-Week Motel.

I didn't want Raven to go. She was smart, pretty, passionately compliant in bed and easy to be around. But I told her the decision was up to her if she wanted to get out before the cold came in a month or so. She said they hadn't decided yet anyway so we didn't have to worry about it and we laid naked under a heavy and battered quilt, the Motel window open, night chill creeping in, David Letterman on the television and her ass pushing against me stirring feelings of need that have still never went away.

Home is where love sits in the corner, alone and never mentioned.

19

I got suspended from the factory for three days for threatening to kick the shit out of some stupid Uncle Fester looking pressman. He was like 6'3" and bald, gap-toothed a real aww shucks motherfucker. He was always reading this pocket size New Testament bible that he kept in the front pocket of his overalls. He'd stand there thumbs hooked in his bib straps and he'd tell everyone how much god hated fags and how Hollywood was trying to turn our kids queer.

I hated that motherfucker.

He used to be an independent preacher at one of them almost snake handler crazy churches that spring up in strip malls all over the rust belt. I remembered something funny about that and one day I went to the library and got the newspaper microfilm and found the frontpage article—he'd been arrested for child pornography. Had 17 video tapes of homemade kiddie porn.

I printed out 20 copies of the article in black and white for 25 cents a copy. Started taping them up above the urinals all over the factory.

Uncle Fester took a stress leave and when he come back he was railing about the Muslims and I had an English copy of the Quran at the Motel room so I brought it to work and started quoting from it and Uncle Fester stole it from my table and threw it away so I called him a kiddie fucker.

He snitched.

That got me wrote up.

When the 53-year-old tired HR lady told me he snitched and she had to write me up I said, "I'm gonna kick the shit outta that kiddie fucker," and that got me a three-day suspension.

I vowed to kick the shit out of him soon anyway as I walked home kicking rocks.

20

I was off for three days and didn't have shit to do. I told Raven to go home and give me a day to myself, and I bought some shrooms and I took a hero's dose, even though I was never great at calculus and I hadn't yet formed any heroes.

I drank some beer and argued with the walls of the motel room. Argued and fought with monsters that lurked in the shadows and lived under the bed in my head.

Drank some water and lay in the quiet, naked, wrapped in a quilt, staring at myself in the dirty mirrors above me. "Maybe this isn't real," my mind roared, and I lay there in the soft folds of a $100-A-Week Motel womb, warm and safe, lost in a temporary world where sadistic, psycho mothers don't convert to Christianity and spend years making their sons pay for their sins.

Everyone at the $100-A-Week Motel is a bastard child of a high school dropout married truck driver with a family of fucking four kids, a rebel flag waving trucker cap wearing real life deacon of a redneck Baptist church, and a schizophrenic mother, barely hanging on to a reality so warped by tragedy that she could never remember who she was supposed to be half the time.

Everyone here was just like that and it felt like a broken network. A family reunion. Almost like home.

I tripped for 16 hours. Laid myself open. Unraveled a year of forced therapy from when I was an angry 14-year-old fighting grown up ghetto projects daydreams.

And then I slept.

Raven came around the next day and we ordered chicken wings and pizza delivered, drank cheap beer, listened to low music, and gently talked of life.

She was an old 25-year-old. On her own since 16. The daughter of a single mother, the daughter of the mother of the coven of castaway witches left to whither in southern swamps.

Her mother taught her all that she knew about divinity and casting hexes on wandering men. She left at 16 and had been trading fortunes and security to lost people in return for her own survival ever since.

I told her a little about my parents. How we had nothing but skeletons in the closet and that hell was real and how you were born into it, stumbled into it, lived through it, but never died to go there.

We got drunk slowly, and steadily and fucked three times but never with any urgency, the traffic continuing outside the motel, with its low grind, the madness that breaks down the hearts and minds of men locked outside all afternoon and evening to where we had a false feeling that everything was ok and we might feel this sheen of euphoria forever.

Home is where we try to become born again, baptized in the glow of cheap digital alarm clocks.

21

I went back to the factory after my three days off. Eugene picked me up right on schedule and I was back to dragging heavy ass pallets of newspaper ads.

The short, fat boss stopped over and asked if I was going to cause any more trouble.

"You're on a short leash kid, and I hate to lose you. You're a goddamn good worker when you ain't fussing and fighting."

I told him I was fine, and shouldered through, back to the grind. Back to the comfort of the 'snick-snick-snick' of pallet jack wheels sliding over factory cement. Back to the 'sa-wick, sa-wick, sa-wick,' of plastic wrap unrolling and tightening around mountains of paper. Back to shoulders hunched against a heavy world, dark with discomfort, but kept at bay with tired muscles and sore backs.

The Uncle Fester fuck kept a wary distance, and by lunch I was back at full speed, and just another living organism swallowed up by a fading industrial revolution.

22

Rudy was kicking it with me one morning before work. He'd ran down to the corner store for me and got a 6-pack and some smokes and a bag of little chocolate donuts. We were sitting outside in a chilly fall morning, drinking a beer and shooting the shit.

Raven was still sleeping, when Moe walked down to us from the office reeking of day-old curry and turmeric laced B.O.

"You no see you neighbors?" he asked, and we fumbled our way through it and agreed that none of us had seen the junkie couple for three days or so.

"Probly run off with no money fo rent," Moe grumbled and left and came back with the keys to the neighbor's room, except they hadn't split to avoid rent. They were dead.

Apparently there was a bad batch of smack going around and they'd had the dumb luck to find it, and they'd both left for their next incarnation, and had left their old ones laying in a $100-A-Week Motel. Maybe, they left to avoid a rent that public universities don't teach in economics classes.

The cops hung around all day, talking to the dredges of humanity that made their temporary residence at the Motel. I called off work hoping dead neighbors would be a good enough excuse to avoid an attendance occurrence at the factory. You only got three a year and I'd already burned two, but how the fuck you going to make it through an eight-hour shift, half drunk and uneasy from hanging out with the cops all day?

Raven knew the dead woman a little. Her name was Donna, she told me. They'd talk sometimes in the evening when I was working. She had three kids and was going to get clean soon, and try to get visitation for the holidays.

I wondered if those kids would miss her? Are heroin

habits more crippling to parenting skills than Christianity? Are tweakers worse parents than drunks?

Me and Raven got drunk, fucked, and fell asleep, angry at a cruel world.

Home is where the sad lives, because it has to live somewhere, too.

23

I did get excused for calling off, but the days with no pay were catching up to me, and I was pretty close to flat busted and down to my last pack of smokes. Eugene loaned me a couple dollars and I bought a Faygo pop and cigarettes for lunch.

It was Wednesday and I didn't get paid til Friday and I thought about that all night.

I could sell my radio at the pawn shop for $10 but that didn't help much and I hated not listening to the radio. There was an alarm clock radio provided by the Motel, but it only got three channels and they barely came in.

I could donate plasma, and get $20, but that was a six-hour day of taking two busses and reading a paperback book forever while community college certificate holders jabbed spikes in your flesh and capitalism mined the resources from your very bloodstream. I hated getting up early and spending all day giving my fluids away for some food. Then having to work all night with a headache because Natty Light does not hydrate like Gatorade.

I couldn't get a payday loan because you needed a checking account for that, and I wasn't allowed to have a checking account. I'd kited checks at every bank stupid enough to let a broken man open an account. Now, they wouldn't even cash my checks for me.

I decided to sell the radio. I would buy it back for $15 on Friday.

24

I sold the radio in the morning, and I had $3.80 in change and I bought a couple packs of smokes, two small bottles, one each for me and Raven after work, a pack of hot dogs, a pack of buns, a bag of generic wavy potato chips, 2 candy bars, and a giant sucker and a plastic rose for Raven.

We made all the hot dogs in a small wok of water on a hot plate I had, and we feasted on cheap filler food, covered with ketchup and mustard and relish and chopped onions ripped from packets from the corner store. We ate till our bellies were full, and drank the last four beers from a case I'd bought two days before, and took a nap, HBO playing a car chase movie on the tv.

We laid around all day, snacking on salty potato chips, and I watched her lay naked for an hour, licking the giant sucker and pretending to be Daddy's best girl. I kissed her on the forehead after, and told her she was.

I showered and rode to work with Eugene, a hot dog and a bun wrapped up in a plastic bag, with ketchup and mustard packets. I had an almost full pack of smokes in my pocket and a sense that I just might make it.

Home is where sustenance fills your spirit.

25

I got promoted to loader after one of the loaders got fired for missing too many days of work, and I got a raise and I was bringing home $350 a week and I felt ok about maybe making it through the winter.

Except the loader job was about as exciting as watching the Jr senator from Wyoming filibuster on C-SPAN.

You stood there for five or six minutes staring at a stack of paper growing taller with each clickety-clack-ack-ack of the metal stacker that spit slippery-as-shit Sunday advertisements out one at time every 1.2 seconds forever and 24 hours a day. I can still hear the clickety-ack sometimes when I'm waiting for the ok-to-cross-the-street signal to change in my favor.

All the press loaders had these beat-to-shit radios patched together with blue collar engineering and bindery glue stolen from the bindery department. They'd listen to the country music channel or the rock channel, and sometimes if you pointed your coat hanger antenna just right you could get the high school football game broadcast on payday Friday nights on the low watt local sports channel and if you stood close you could hear the senior cheerleaders kicking pom poms across the buckling concrete parking lots of pretend they don't exist inner city abortion clinics. All the cheerleaders I've ever known grow up to have bellies. None of the junkie girls do. I report this observation without judgement as I have been guilty of chasing them both through rust belt trailer parks.

High school football is stupid if your hometown never loved you. So I bought this disc man at the pawn shop for $20 and I borrowed some books on tape CDs from the local library and I listened to East of Eden and roared with ole Sam'l Hamilton, and spent a lot of dead dick factory hours wondering why Cathy was the character that I thought of the most.

The short, fat boss came by and told me I wasn't supposed to listen to headphones cuz OSHA said I wouldn't hear fork lifts coming and would surely have my entrails smeared across shipping dock B.

I calmly explained that no fucking forklifts could fit between these 13 ton steel fucking printing presses which is why we were all breaking our fucking backs pallet-jacking sumo wrestler sized stacks of paper all over the goddamned maze the idiot fucking engineers set up by squeezing as much Sunday ad printing machines into as little space as fucking possible, and besides, let's be real you short motherfucker, if OSHA walked into this shit-hole factory you'd have worse fucking problems than my headphones.

"Don't call me short," he huffed, but he stomped the fuck away.

And everyone kind of left me alone.

I listened to three audio books a week. Life might be ok. Maybe I could make it here in this midwestern quicksand trap of work til you drop chasing undefined American dreams.

Eugene and I split a pint bottle of wild turkey I'd splurged on when I got my first big loader pay raise check.

"I'm moving to a boarding house tomorrow," he said, looking straight ahead at the tired old burgundy door of room number 11 of the $100-A-Week Motel.

"Eugene," I said, turning to look at him, "you gonna break yo momma's heart."

"Ima tell her tomorrow. I already paid $65 for the week."

I drank wild turkey. Smoked a square. Laughing into the nearly dead November night.

26

Tone and Sheila's old room was empty for about three weeks after the orphaned junkies were adopted by a cruel cosmic father everyone calls God.

Then Jesus moved in one day.

Jesus was 6'2" or some shit, skinny, had long frizzy hair down to his ass. There were rabbits' feet tied on the ends of his hair. He had a mountain man beard and hairy legs.

Jesus wore dresses. A blue and plaid one, or rainbow striped one, that always came down to just above his potato lump knees.

I'd seen Jesus walking around before. He walked everywhere. Always wore headphones but no one ever saw them connected to anything. Everyone knew who he was cuz they'd see him walking, tall and skinny, long hair and wild dress, both waving in the wind. Everyone called him Jesus because that's what you call middle aged crazy men with long hair and a beard. I've known three men that society called Jesus. None of them turned tap water into wine.

Turns out this Jesus' real name was Randy, but Randy died in Vietnam. Jesus wouldn't tell me how. It took me a few times trying to talk to him to figure any of it out.

Jesus wore dresses because women could wear pants, so why can't men wear dresses? Raven tried to give him a silk scarf, and he laughed and refused it.

"Men don't wear those," he said.

He walked to the Wrangler roast beef every day and bought 2 roast beef sandwiches, and a root beer for lunch. Every damn day, I'd watch him eat it in front of his room, then he'd get up and take off walking somewhere else. I'd come home with Eugene at midnight and we'd see ole Jesus walking down dark streets, those bare legs ignoring November frost.

Jesus gave me the blessing of eternal life once, because I gave him a Marlboro. I've been uncomfortable about that for a long time. That kind of threat can put a hopeless man on the brink.

Home is where you wonder about eternity.

27

Eugene didn't tell his momma about the boarding house the next day, or the day after that either. He kept threatening empty promises every afternoon while we chugged along on our way to the factory in his little rusty Chevette.

It was mid-November, and we had taken to wearing long-sleeved, thermal shirts under our t-shirts, and winter stocking caps on our heads. They'd leave the dock doors open half the fucking night and if you weren't prepared you'd freeze your ears and nut-sack off.

Eugene was still working as a labeler, and factory rednecks were still fucking with him all the time. But there was this tough lady named Trudy that worked as a loader on the opposite side of the plant from us, and I noticed that she was coming down to our side at break time and her and Eugene would share cigarettes and talk.

Trudy was about 5'4" tall, probably 180 pounds, and looked like she played roller derby in her late teens, was covered in kitchen tattoos, cut her hair short, and would have been a good ole corn fed midwestern gal if not for being tougher than a three-legged junk yard dog. I bet she was 35, but she looked 40, and hanging out with ole tall, skinny awkward Eugene (I mean, the dude tucked his fucking t-shirt into his Dickie's work jeans and shit and carried a handkerchief in his back pocket) was pretty much the most amusing thing I had to think about in a dead dick November factory.

After a few days of them sharing smokes and wordless conversations, a couple of us smokers saw them kiss and Eugene walked past us back inside, looking straight ahead, his face splotching red with embarrassment and the excitement of whole new worlds unfolding right in front of him.

That was Eugene Kevin Anderson's first kiss. Goofy fucker was 25 goddamn years old, and his momma was losing hold of him, and she didn't even have a fucking clue yet.

28

It was the Sunday before thanksgiving, and me and Raven were laying in bed, bellies full, hearts warm and brains drunk and high on booze, weed and love.

We'd went to the mall that afternoon, bought some discount rack books at the lights too bright, elevator-music-heart, mall bookstore, a black and purple cardigan sweater and black mini skirt at a teen girl goth store place for Raven, a half-pound bag of way too strong and sophisticated for the $100-A-Week Motel fresh ground coffee beans for me, and a black Ramones winter beanie, also for me.

I carried our shopping bags around a shiny Sunday mall, teenagers looking cool, peacocking boys with spiked hair and thick wanna be gold chains. Teenager girls wearing makeup they hoped made them look mature and experienced, though it did neither. Youth is something you cannot, and probably should not, cover up anyway, but no one fucking knows that when they're 16.

I kept watching Raven glide around mall floors too heavily glossed with 5am wax jobs, so much so that the floors would live forever sporting a dull shine that even rampant capitalism could never kill.

I kept watching other people watch Raven. Men and women looked, turned away, then looked back slowly with their chins tucked so as not to be obvious. Raven had the It. The magical pull of pure open human-ness, the It of organic wonder and joy. She had the It of a reckless innocence which might have been the most magical part. The it of innocence despite three human broken hearts' worth of emotional scars.

Men and women turned and looked, even though they did not know why. Raven, oblivious to all of it except the moment.

The now, right in front of her face. Moving from store front to store front. Grabbing my arm. Kissing my cheek. Oohing and ahhing or hissing and mocking (the midwestern suburban middle management clothing stores) And she had no energy left to see the wake of broken dreams her hips and ass created.

We got two buckets of fried chicken to go and two giant chocolate chip cookies from the corporate cookie kiosk manned by a teenaged girl with too mature makeup.

We rode home on the bus, the November late afternoon slipping into early dark evening. Raven had my headphones on. She was listening to a Prince CD. Her hood up on her hoodie. Her head laying against my chest. Her eyes closed. Her lips wet, and full and smiling.

I looked out the bus window at graffitied bus benches and busted concrete curbs. Neon lights from pawn shops and payday loan shops. Neon lights blurring from liquor store windows protected by metal grates.

I'd never had a thing I could call my own, except a stubborn and thus far unbreakable will to live and a dumb work ethic that I'd never seen matched.

I was trying to remember the words to "Bluebird" by Bukowski. At a red light, a poor man's strip joint staring me in the eyes. Diesel bus exhaust hanging in dying winter air. My heart felt like humming a little love song, but I tried hard to be too tough for it.

And now, we lay in bed, Sunday night football muted in the dark and Raven turned to me and kissed me.

"The troupe is talking about leaving again. There's a cheap place down in Biloxi. They want to leave next week," she said.

And I turned deaf. The bluebird inside of me bit his tongue and began to struggle to breathe in a heart turning to stone.

Home is where the roof caves in on a should have known better heart.

29

The days before a holiday weekend, and especially the days before the Thanksgiving Holiday weekend are good days in a factory. There's an air of camaraderie and cheer, the excitement of paid days off, and long weekends, and sleeping in with lazy lovers, afternoons with strong coffee looming just ahead, hours with nothing to do but not give a fuck about no goddamned factory.

Press teams grouped together and brought in potlucks, steaming crock pots, and foil wrapped aluminum trays, and store-bought cakes and cookies, and a dozen two liters of all the cola company war's misfortunate children available.

But I went through it in a kind of comfortable numbness. A shock. The automatic response of experiencing the days after an earthquake, a tornado, a hurricane. On autopilot, smiling and nodding at the efforts of cheer your tired neighbors are putting forth, reminding yourself they're all doing the best they can, too, to survive the ravages and effects of lost generations dead in forgotten factories.

Eugene had finally moved out to the boarding house. Him and Trudy had went on two real life motherfucking dates, and Eugene was reluctant to say much, but he'd apparently fumbled his way to second base.

He told me he was gonna take Trudy over to his mom's house on Thanksgiving, to have dinner with his grandparents and mom and her two yapping mop head dogs. And I felt a moment of gratitude that all I had to do was wonder if I was going to survive this goddamned Howling Wolf Blues song November.

I closed my eyes that last car ride home with Eugene. The last before Thanksgiving. 11:30pm on Wednesday night the eve of football and fat turkeys, and it was 3am some random

Saturday night in some outpost juke joint, and I was tired and drunk, my throat sore from three packs of cowboy lungs a day, dark and smoky with the weary holding on of just enough fucks left to perk up as Ole Howling Wolf moans "How many more years, have I got to let you dog me around."

I gave Eugene our departing ritual fist bump with my own street preacher blessing of "be safe," and I looked up and saw Raven standing in the window of room number 11 of the $100-A-Week Motel, the raggedy and tired, probably used to be a curtain pushed aside, just like every night. Raven waiting for Daddy to come home. Take his boots off. Kisses, and tight hugs.

Raven standing in the window wearing one of my thermal shirts and absolutely nothing else, of which I learned about seven seconds after I shut that tired old once upon a time burgundy Motel door, and about four seconds before I locked the sonofabitch.

Four days I thought. Raven and the wandering troupe of trying to make it in a world that has never pretended to care about traveling artists were gonna leave on Monday.

Four days I thought as we made our welcome home toast of lit blunts, and cracked cold canned beers, our welcome home toast of hey, look you motherfuckers, we made it through one more day.

Four more of these days and nights.

30

That Thanksgiving was the best one I've ever had. Me and Raven, and all the misfit orphans that weren't invited to real family Thanksgiving dinners decided to hang out down in the wandering troupe's rooms. A $100-A-Week Motel potluck extravaganza that ended up so beautiful and full of laughter, the likes of which hadn't been witnessed by desperate Motel walls in all the years that it had pretended to be a real working motel, combined.

Me and Raven went down to the corner store, and bought the last four packs of turkey sandwich slices they had back in the refrigerator door area of the place. We bought all the cans of croissant rolls they had, too, and two boxes of pumpkin flavored Lil' Debbie snack cakes. I bought a case of beer, two bottles of pineapple champagne, even though champagne tickled my nose when I drank it, and it tasted like a fancy person was too scared to drink a damn beer. I bought the champagne because this seemed like a celebration. And I bought a bottle of wine, a case of beer, and to show I was really ready for a good time, I bought a gallon bottle of cheap whisky.

The party kicked off about two and we feasted, me and Raven, and the wandering no longer called gypsies, and Rudy was there, and Jesus even stopped in, Eugene and Trudy came through, a few other Motel deviants and even Moe came down with his wife, a pretty young Arab girl, her hair covered appropriately for her husband's god, and they had their little boy with them, a skinny, shy dark haired, dark eyed little fella, and I was in such a good mood I gave Moe's little boy this Michael Jordan basketball card I had propped up on a shelf above my tv, before he went back with his momma to their little Motel room home, where Moe's wife washed their clothes in the bathtub by hand, and hung them on a rigged clothes line Moe had paid some crackhead handy man to put up behind the Motel. A little Motel room home, where Moe and his family ate from a wok and microwave and watched American cartoons, and where a little Arab boy would grow up wearing navy blue t-shirts proclaiming his love of America, even though he would always be puzzled about why no one ever believed him. I hope he still has that Michael Jordan card. I checked. It's worth about a thousand bucks if it's in good shape. Hope he was better at protecting long-term investments than me.

Moe couldn't drink because his parent's god didn't allow it, but he came back by the bathroom with me and Raven and Rudy, and we chiefed a blunt together, and ole motherfucking Rudy pulled out his pipe and we all chipped away at small rocks of paradise. We set the Motel room smoke alarm off with all our happiness, and fucking Moe ripped the fucker off the wall, and spiked it like a football, yelling and celebrating like a running back that had just scored the winning touchdown in a family turkey day flag football Super Bowl. The fucking smoke alarm gave up its ghost and splintered in about nine pieces. Do Motel smoke alarms get another shot at another incarnation? Or do they die, forgotten, even after all those years of watching over America's unfortunate sons?

We laughed, that laughter I told you about. The kind that no one was accustomed to hearing pouring out of a cheap, quickly eroding, rusty ole Motel off a major four-lane road that ran through the rough part of town.

I had a taste for more of that paradise that Rudy always chased, and I sent him off with $30 to get whatever he could get for it, and I hung outside with Jesus. He'd taken a break from pacing around his real home, the neighborhood. Maybe he was seeking his disciples, and maybe they were chasing a different paradise.

We made croissants in my convection oven, two at a time for 10 minutes, then we'd take them out and slice 'em open, and stuff 'em with turkey slices and imitation cheese slices, and put 'em back in for 90 seconds, watching the imitation cheese wilt, but never melt. Imitation cheese is almost tough enough to be a resident in a $100-A-Week motel.

We watched football and slept in on Friday, and drank beer, and Saturday after Thanksgiving me and Raven took the bus to the golden arches a few blocks from the downtown art museum, and we ate pancakes off Styrofoam plates. We walked down to the museum, free admission on Saturdays, and we wandered hand in hand through sacred hallways that lay empty and abandoned. Forgotten holy relics made by holy humans. I bought Raven some knee-high Starry Night socks, and we pretended that this wasn't what it was, an effort to squeeze the last moments we had into hours that meant something.

We drank and relaxed and watched football all weekend, and on Monday morning after the best Thanksgiving I ever had, I got up at 6am and made the last half pot of my good coffee, and I helped Raven load her weird moving trunk into a battered short bus, and the birds that were too stupid to realize it was time to move back south whistled tv static, and traffic see-sawed back and forth.

I drank the last of the gallon of cheap whiskey, looked at the three paperback books sitting on a battered $100-A-Week Motel nightstand. My eyes blurred but I was too young and stupid to realize that it was ok to hurt a little, when what you thought might be sunshine disappeared behind the half empty strip mall three blocks down a tired midwestern four-lane road.

I sat outside with Jesus, while he ate roast beef sandwiches, and asked no one how it was possible to be this tired, this young.

Jesus said, "You know I ain't really Jesus, man," and I laughed.

Home is where you wonder who Jesus really is, man.

31

Eugene picked me up on Monday after Thanksgiving, and we went to work, thermal undershirts, and me in my new Ramones beanie, that was already making itself permanently at home on my head.

Shiny magazine ad inserts don't know anything about heartbreak. They don't know anything about tiredness, or aching shoulders, aching backs, aching feet.

Factories don't know anything about lonely holidays, or empty midnight motel room beds. Factories don't know about ashtrays that overflow with twisted cigarette butts and manic early mornings when the ghosts of dead and gone away lovers offer comfort that isn't real, yet you'll seek it out on the ripples of cheap beer drunks and Grateful Dead sunrises over Motel dumpsters. Morning dew rising from strong coffee, eyes numb to clear cold sunrays.

Factories can't know a goddamn thing about a heart bleeding slowly to death, on a 30-year suicide plan, fueled by angry wine and an already morning cough from these goddamned cigarettes. Jesus I needed to cut back. Fuckers were over two bucks a fucking pack now. Factories can't know about this shit, because they're machines.

That's the thing about machines. They're made of metal and concrete, re-bar, and cement, and corrugated aluminum, and steel girders every 30 feet, and they're made with no heart, so they can only come alive by harvesting the heartbeats of desperate people living paycheck to paycheck and subsisting on frozen mac n cheese dinners from corner gas stations.

Factories can only live by harvesting those heartbeats, and in doing so, can only survive by draining away the strongest years of your strongest heart, so that when you finally get a chance,

IF you finally get a chance to crawl away from that goddamned machine, you're left with the remnants and clippings of reel-to-reel flashbacks of the passions of your youth, and a heart, weak from working six days a week, feeding the machine. A heart weak, but limping along, through humid southern retirement trailer parks that sold plastic dreams to midwestern factory rats.

Eugene picked me up and told me he'd gotten laid finally, but even that couldn't reignite any feelings of hope in a dead man's heart.

A heart draining from long factory hours, and short flings with women that never intended to learn how to love, not even on accident.

32

I made it through a stupid, bright winter December. Had regular chats with my own personal Jesus, both the neighbor and the one that hung above the bed in my head.

Raven had left me a leather notebook that had a leather string that wrapped around and kept it tied shut. I finally opened it during a long lonely drunk Christmas weekend. She'd written me a goodbye note on the first couple of pages.

"Daddy,

I know that you know I found your notebooks of poetry. You probably don't know that I read them all the time when you were at work in the factory. I've had this notebook for a while. You should use it to write in. Use your gel pens that you like. It's made of hemp parchment. The gel ink will bleed into the pages. Don't drink too much. Keep an eye on Rudy.

all my love,
Raven"

I read it twice. Put the leather book down and got a beer, and looked out the motel window, the tired drapery pushed aside, like it had been so many times, by so many guests.

There was nothing to look at. Just rusty Toyota cars held together by bungee cords and camouflage duct tape. Rusty street signs. Dead, brown weeds clinging to hardscrabble cracked curbs. Do weeds get a chance at another incarnation after slow December deaths? Or do they simply crumble away after inspiring the broken stanzas of so many motel room artists?

I looked at the nothing anyway.

Home is where there is nothing, but you.

33

It finally happened. It was a Wednesday, the middle of a dead gray, dirty snow-covered late January week. Me and Eugene had drank tall boys in the gas station parking lot, in his freezing Chevette, 40 minutes before our factory shift. We'd shared a quarter roach I had in the coin pocket of my Dickie's work jeans, four hits apiece and a yellow burn spot on each of our thumbs. The poor smoke their joints til they hurt. Til they burn. They smoke them til their skin melts because they need all the medical services the smoke can possibly provide.

Eugene told me Trudy wanted him to move into her studio apartment, but he was worried about the bed wetting. She couldn't visit his boarding house room. The crazy old lady that ran it wouldn't let the opposite sex hang out because she had been a victim of free love in 1953, and she knew it's long-term effects.

Trudy only had a day bed, so Eugene used that as his last grasp excuse, but he was getting laid damn near every night, and in spite of his current predicament might have been the most content man I'd ever known.

We walked in properly medicated, and braced against a long night of 'clackety-ack' and 'sa-wick sa-wick' and it finally happened.

The kiddie fucker Uncle Fester fuck was yelling at Eugene over in the break area about how whoring around was gonna send him to hell, and Eugene just sat there not looking at nothing and letting spittle assault his ear hairs. And I snapped like I did once a year since I first picked up a brick.

I'd had enough of the kiddie fucker's bullshit, and enough of the factory's dead dick late nights. All the fire that had ever raged in my burned-out heart came roaring back and I picked ole

Uncle Fester up and slammed him on his fucking bald ass head onto the cold hard factory concrete floor. The kiddie fucker got knocked the fuck out, and two loaders grabbed me and dragged me back, and we all fell onto that cold concrete floor, piled in a knot of holy shit, I can't believe this is happening.

I'll never forget, mid fall that cracked my head and bled a little, but not more than a 12-pack couldn't numb, mid-fall, in slow motion seeing ole Eugene rise up from a crooked wooden picnic table, and stab his bony finger into the fading afternoon and yelling, actually fucking yelling "Jesus loves me. He told me so. He lives in room 13 of the $100-A-Week Motel, and he's my friend. My name is Eugene Kevin Anderson and I have friends."

And I smiled as my head split.

I saw the short, fat boss come running sideways out of his glass cubicle and standing over us, panting and bleeding factory brothers, screaming and hollering and I knew, that I was done here. Ole Uncle Fester groaned asleep still. He'd be just fine in a day or two, but they tell me he quit a month later, and left town and nobody knows where the creep disappeared to.

No one has ever told me thank you for ridding them of him. Just as well I guess. Any nod of gratitude to a blue-collar American man makes him feel indebted. I know. I've been stuck here in this midwestern Ohio city for 17 years now. I'll never fully leave. I owe them too much.

34

I got drunk, slow and for a week, and watched late night basketball games and late night tv show comics, and thought about what to do next.

I put my stolen library books in a stolen milk crate and left them in front of the library, and I got on a greyhound bus in Effingham, IL with a duffle bag with some Dickie's work jeans. Some t-shirts and two truckers hats in it, and a stolen copy of Still Life with Woodpecker because I wasn't sure if I'd be able to find one in the boarding house I'd heard about in Jacksonville. I'd heard there's a bunch of factories around it and I knew that I'd get there, and I'd work my way into one of them, and I'd give away some more of my heartbeats for a chance to keep on hanging on til I could figure out what it was a cosmic god and a next-door neighbor Jesus were trying to teach me.

I had a $176 in my pocket, and some pretty good work boots on my feet with several more months of life left in them. I had three pairs of new socks still in the plastic. Sam, the Arab owner of the corner store gave them to me as a parting gift. Fucking Moe gave me a hug. His dark-haired son a fist bump. I told him my street preacher blessing, "be safe."

I drank from small bottles of cheap wine, and wondered if the beach in Florida was warm enough to swim in, in the middle of February. I was going to find out.

Home…is a $100-A-Week Motel.

EDITOR'S ACKNOWLEDGEMENTS

The first time I heard Dan Denton read, a little voice inside my head said, *this is what it's all about. This is why we read and this is why we write because our lives are better for it.*

Hearing Dan Denton read was a wake-up call for me. During a global pandemic when nothing has been quite sure for anyone, I am quite sure about Dan Denton's writing, every word of every line in every paragraph is rich and beautiful and filled with heart.

Denton lives in Toledo Ohio where he works in a factory and reads and writes on his breaks tucked away where no one can see him. He writes about the music of the factories and the motels and the bars, and the people. And I swear I can still hear the music long after I've read his words.

Thank you so much to S.A. Griffin for his powerful foreword and for all he does for our literary community at large.

A big thank you to Michele McDannold who is a magical force in and unto herself, and a key part of Punk Hostage Press, without whom this book would have never happened. I could thank the pandemic, but that will never happen, no matter how true it is. And thank you to Dan Denton for his dedication and his words and his powerful spirit. I am honored to publish his first book, and hopefully, many more to come.

Iris Berry
Los Angeles
January 1, 2021

AUTHOR'S ACKNOWLEDGEMENTS

My deepest gratitude goes to:

Iris Berry for discovering me, and for believing in me. For her dozens of hours of planning and layout work. Her countless hours on the phone telling me how the publishing process works. And for telling the best Hollywood stories of Punk Rock, Bukowski, Bob Forrest and underground poetry. For sending me hundreds of dollars in free books that I have devoured on up-too-late work nights, hair on fire, alive in reading them.

Thank you for everything, Iris. September 20 babies rock!

Michele McDannold for vouching for me to Iris. For introducing the two of us in a kismet kind of way. For always being my champion, my creative sister, my mentor, my co-mentee. For always putting me front and center, feature reading with America's best outlaw poets in epic underground festivals. For believing in me when I wasn't yet convinced I was a writer.

Thank you. Thank you for everything.

SA Griffin, for working tirelessly to spread the gospel of poetry. For being one of my earliest, and longest heroes as a writer.

For editing the very Bible that has carried the underground spirit to me and countless other lost poets.

Thank you for everything, and especially thank you for making some of my dreams come true in agreeing to be a part of this book.

My wife, Elizabeth. My lover. My friend. My editor. My promoter. My biggest fan. The artist of my life. Thank you for being you, and allowing me to be me. For being patient. For encouraging the madness. For understanding the madness.

My children, for somehow loving me and supporting me in their own ways. For being the best, most creative young humans I've ever known.

Michael Grover and Bob Phillips, for taking me on with unspoken terms, as a student of poetry. You both have taught me more about poetry, and life, than all the creative writing instructors in the Mattoon School district.

The Toledo artist community: Adrian, Jonie, Autumn, Craig James, Stormi, Miriam, Drew, Trina, Ezhno, Patrick, Ryan, Ben, Vester, Kerry, and Rebel...countless others, for accepting me as an artist. And for helping me along the journey.

The old guys (and one slightly older than me cosmic sister) at the sick table at the Chapter V Club. John M. Bill S. Kelly C. Kevin C. Bill C. One Arm Tom. Erin K. And especially John Z. The chairman. For teaching me how to stay alive long enough to let the magic happen.

I love you all.
Dan Denton ~ 2021

At the age of 13, Dan Denton read an original ode to Jesus at an evangelical church camp in Alabama. The Christians loved it so much that an elderly minister felt called by God to anoint young Denton as a consecrated vessel to do God's work for the rest of his life.

Denton became an atheist, and frequented under-ground punk shows and stole books from libraries. But who's to say that living a gutter drunk life in his early 20s, and reading back alley poems to the homeless isn't God's work? Who's to say that screaming broken stanzas over the grind of an assembly line isn't a layman's Gospel? That smuggling paperbacks in lunch buckets past sleeping factory secruity guards isn't the work of a missionary?

After losing all his poems and stories a half dozen times to homelessness, vengeful ex-lovers, and general vagrancy, Denton finally graduated from what might be his last rehab, and found salvation in strong coffee and concrete factory floors.

His writing has been published online, and in print journals, in multiple newspapers, and anthologies. He has two previous chapbooks; *Bury My Heart in the Gutter* (EMP Press, 2018) and *Give Us This Day Our Daily Grind: an Ode to the American Factory Worker* (Lunch Bucket Brigade, 2020.) He has read his poetry in support of 100k poets for change in multiple states and has read at underground poetry festivals with some of America's best outlaw poets.

Jeep

MORE ABOUT *$100-A-WEEK MOTEL*

Everyone has a story to tell in this American blanket of individual threads. Even the threads that seem least significant. Sometimes those are the best stories. It is my experience to be at the bottom makes the best story, and surely you have a story to tell. We are fortunate to hear Dan Denton's story here. Told as clear as the Bukowski or Hunter S. Thompson that influenced him. But this is not their story. They just prepared Dan to tell it. This is Dan's story of life at the bottom. The side that America is not so proud to show. But it is essential that we get it out there.

Michael Grover, author of *Heavy Metal*

Dan Denton's *$100-A-Week Motel* was hands down one of the most riveting reads I had in 2020. His writing style easily transported me to drab, bleak yet hopeful world of this story. His portraying the humanity of the colorful, wayward characters showed me the humanity of us all, but especially myself. If you can see and appreciate the love, passion, hope, determination, and dignity in the people of the *$100 A Week Motel*, you have effectively learned empathy and thus have become a better person. This is reading for your soul.

Audamatik

MORE ABOUT *$100-A-WEEK MOTEL*

$100-A-Week Motel is blunt, no-bullshit prose backed by a skid-row, punk-rock gospel choir of fuck-ups and goners. This isn't a novel, it's a gritty collection of rust-belt psalms, bite-sized pieces of poverty, desperation, and humanity that lodge themselves in your windpipe and refuse to leave. It chokes you with compassion and second-hand smoke. *$100-A-Week Motel* has an honesty that only comes from experience. It's the hangdog mope down to the bar, head still pumping with a week-long hangover. It's a drunken saunter through the rough part of town, whistling past the graveyard and factory, chasing the sad-eyed moon.

A.S. Coomer, author of *Memorabilia* & *The Fetishists*

MORE PUNK HOSTAGE PRESS BOOKS

Fractured (2012) by **Danny Baker**

By **A. Razor**
Better Than A Gun In A Knife Fight (2012)
Drawn Blood: Collected Works From D.B.P.LTD., 1985-1995 (2012)
Beaten Up Beaten Down (2012)
Small Catastrophes In A Big World (2012)
Half-Century Status (2013).
Days Of Xmas Poems (2014)
Puro Purismo (2021)

By **Iris Berry**
The Daughters Of Bastards (2012)
All That Shines Under The Hollywood Sign (2019)

Impress (2012) by **C.V. Auchterlonie**

Tomorrow, Yvonne - Poetry & Prose For Suicidal Egoists (2012)
by **Yvonne De la Vega**

Miracles Of The Blog: A Series (2012) **by Carolyn Srygley- Moore**

8th & Agony (2012) by **Rich Ferguson**

By **Jack Grisham**
Untamed (2013)
Code Blue: A Love Story ~ Limited Edition (2014)
Code Blue: The Hide Under the Mattress Edition (2020)

By **Dennis Cruz**
Moth Wing Tea (2013)
The Beast Is We (2018)

Blood Music (2013) by **Frank Reardon**

Showgirl Confidential (2013) by **Pleasant Gehman**

Yeah, Well... (2014) by **Joel Landmine**

MORE PUNK HOSTAGE PRESS BOOKS

Stealing The Midnight From A Handful Of Days (2014)
by **Michele McDannold**

History Of Broken Love Things (2014) by **SB Stokes**

Dreams Gone Mad With Hope (2014) by **S.A. Griffin**

How To Take A Bullet And Other Survival Poems (2014)
by **Hollie Hardy**

Dead Lions (2014) by **A.D. Winans**

By **Nadia Bruce-Rawlings**
Scars (2014)
Driving in the Rain (2020)

WHEN I WAS A DYNAMITER, Or, how a Nice Catholic Boy Became a Merry Prankster, a Pornographer, and a Bridegroom Seven Times (2014) by **Lee Quarnstrom**

By **Alexandra Naughton**
I Will Always Be Your Whore/Love Songs For Billy Corgan (2014)
You Could Never Objectify Me More Than I've Already Objectified Myself (2015)

No Parachutes To Carry Me Home (2015) by **Maisha Z Johnson**

#1 Son And Other Stories (2017) by **Michael Marcus**

LOOKING FOR JOHNNY, The Legend of Johnny Thunders (2018)
by **Danny Garcia**

Burden Of Concrete (2020) by **William S. Hayes**

Dillinger's Thompson (2020) by **Todd Moore**

Made in USA - Kendallville, IN
32645_9781940213125
03.15.2022 1519